Tidy Up

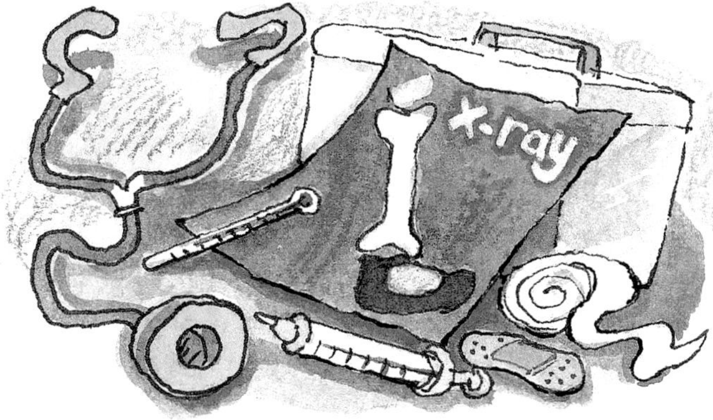

Monica Hughes
Illustrated by Lisa Smith

RIGBY

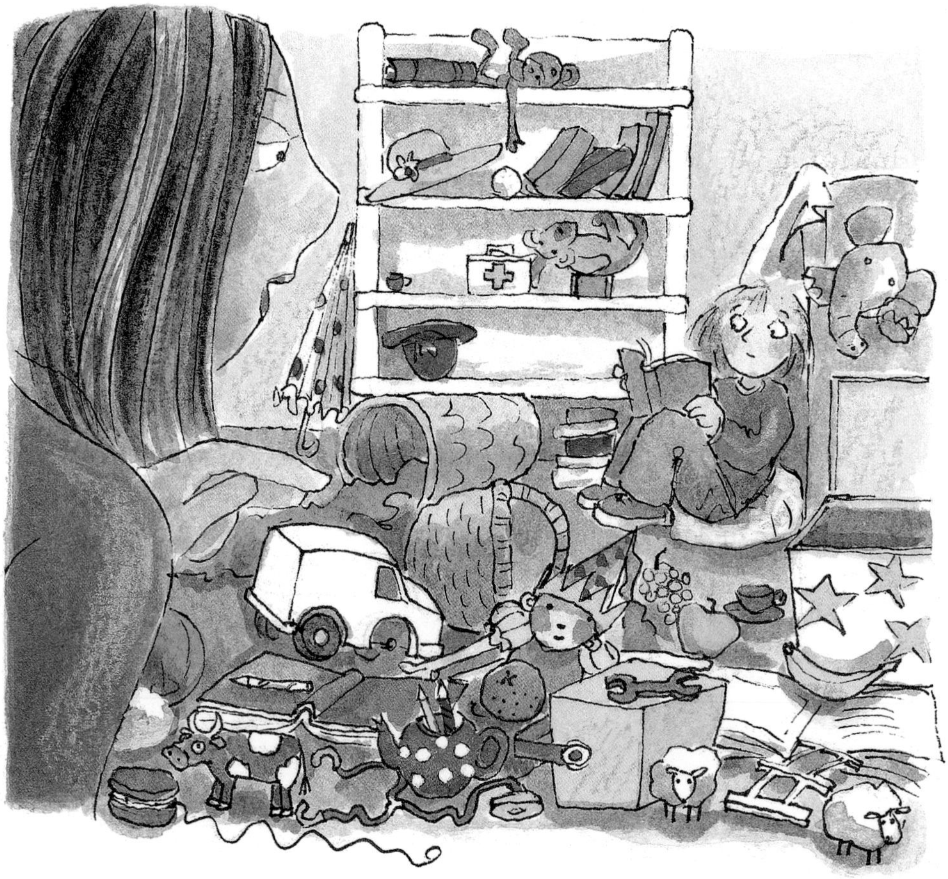

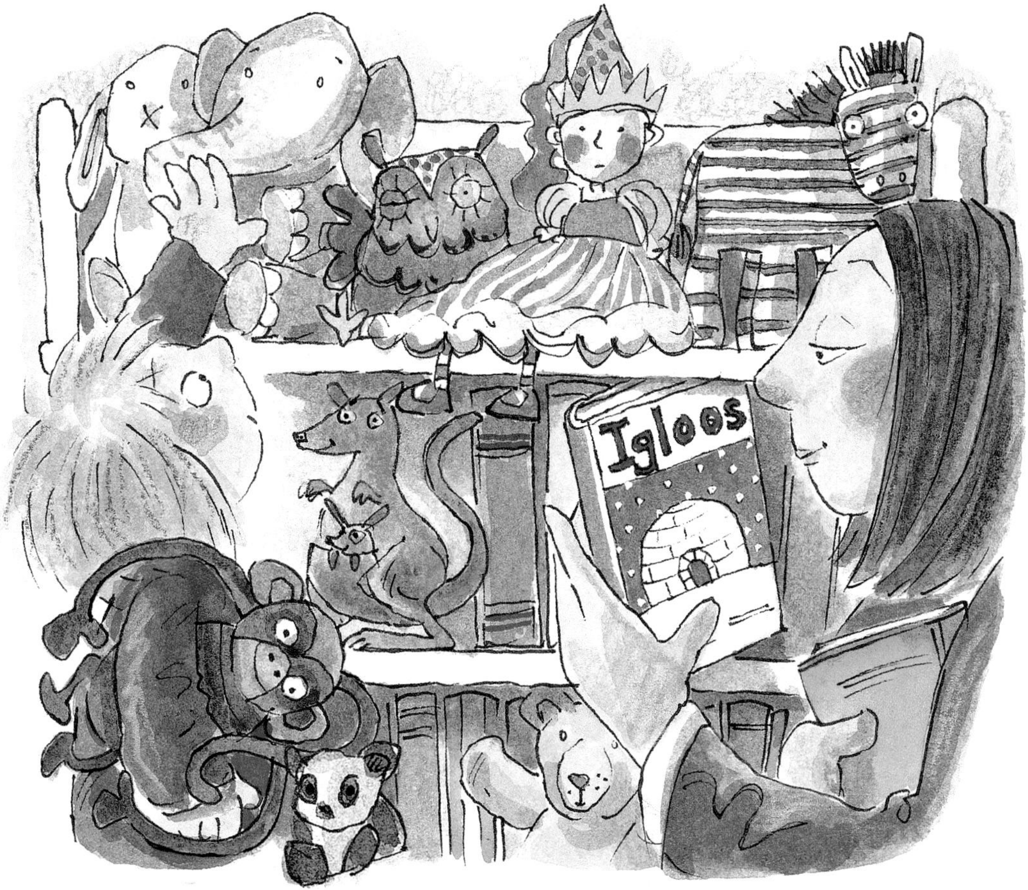
Igloos

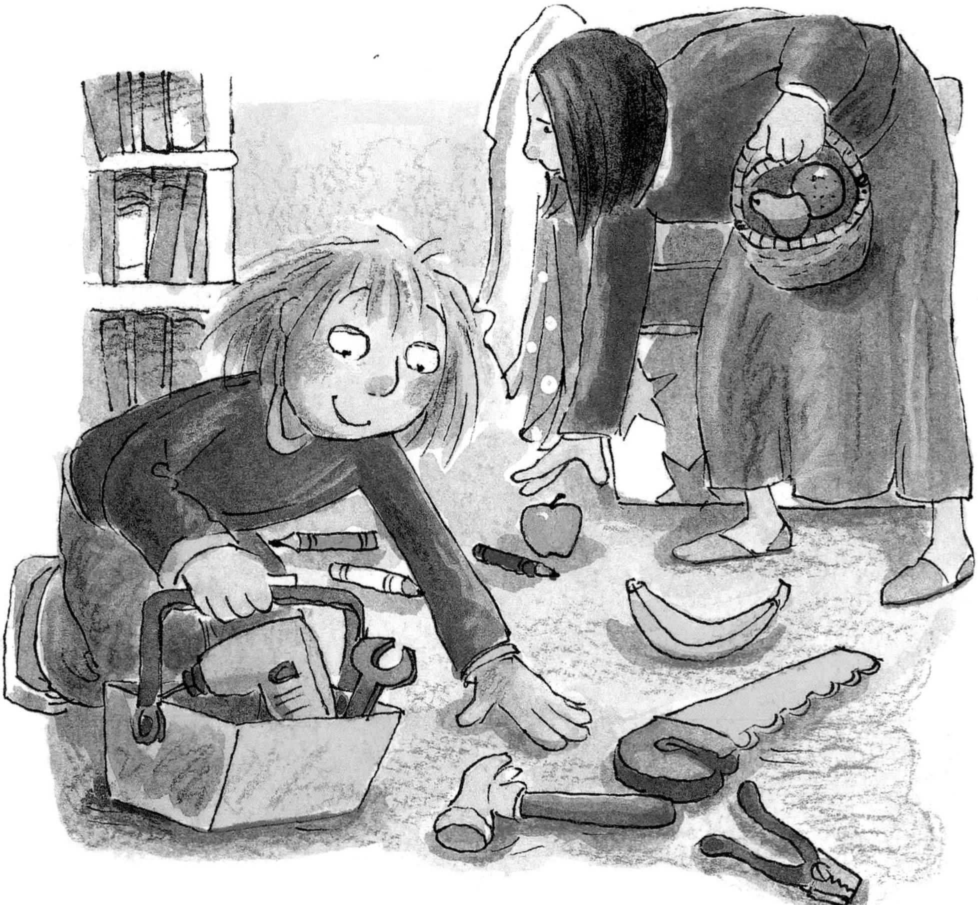

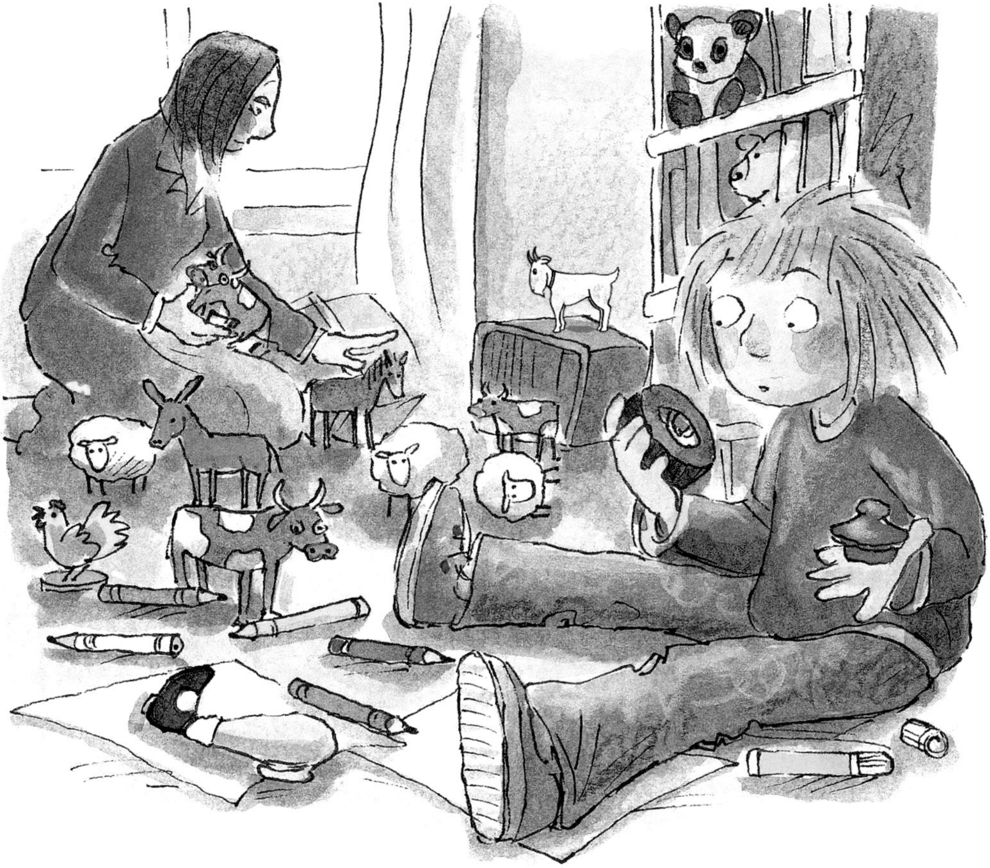

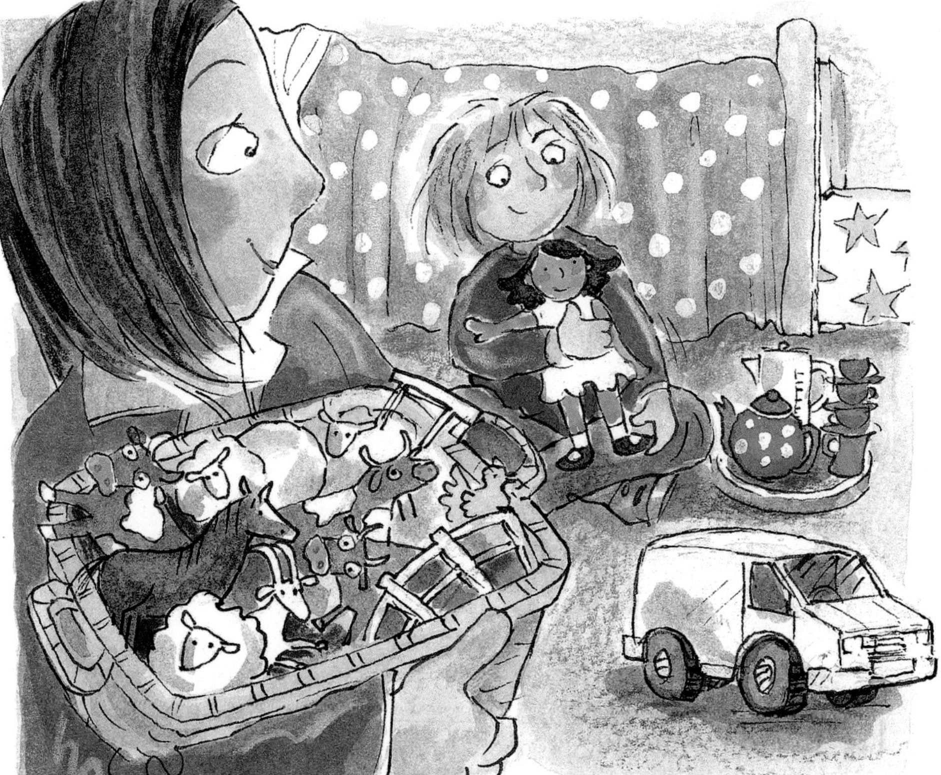

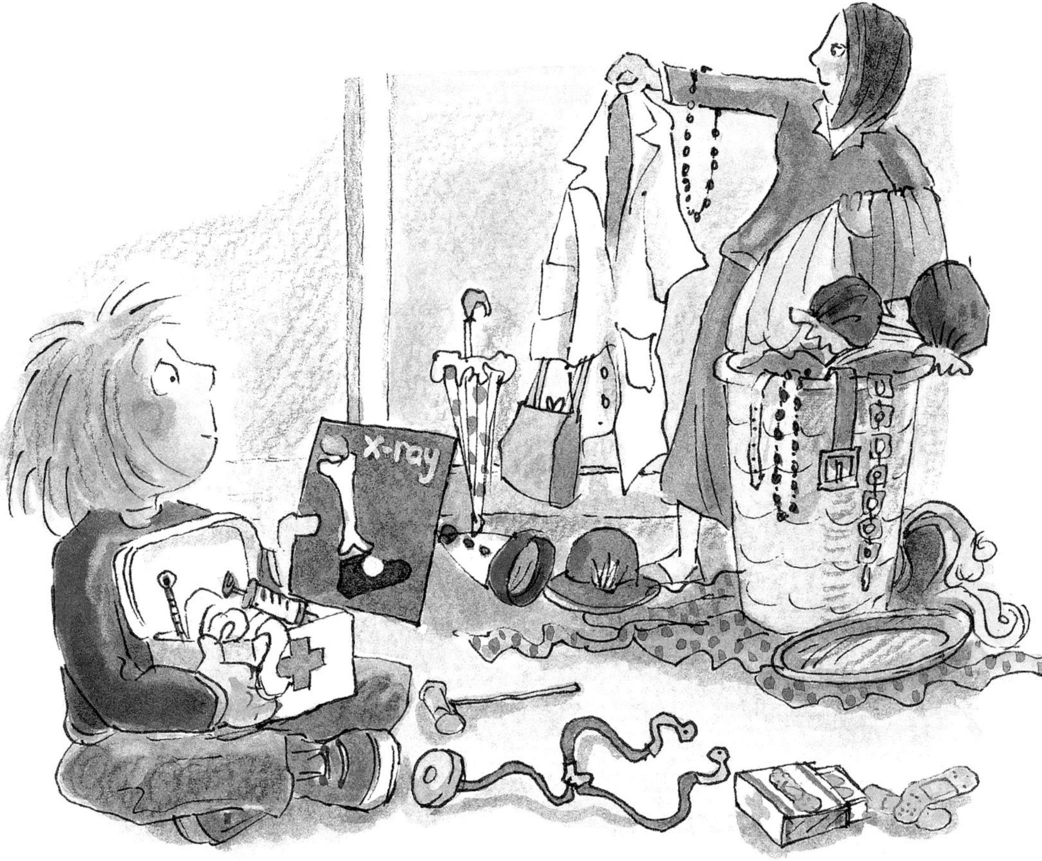
x-ray

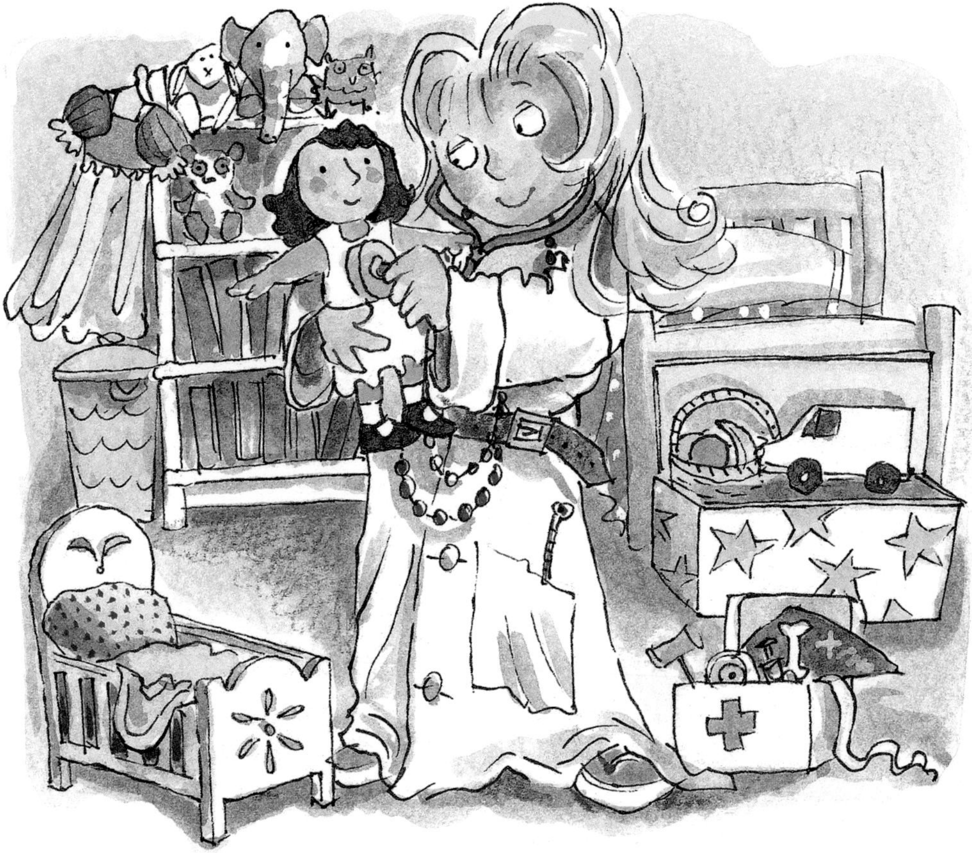